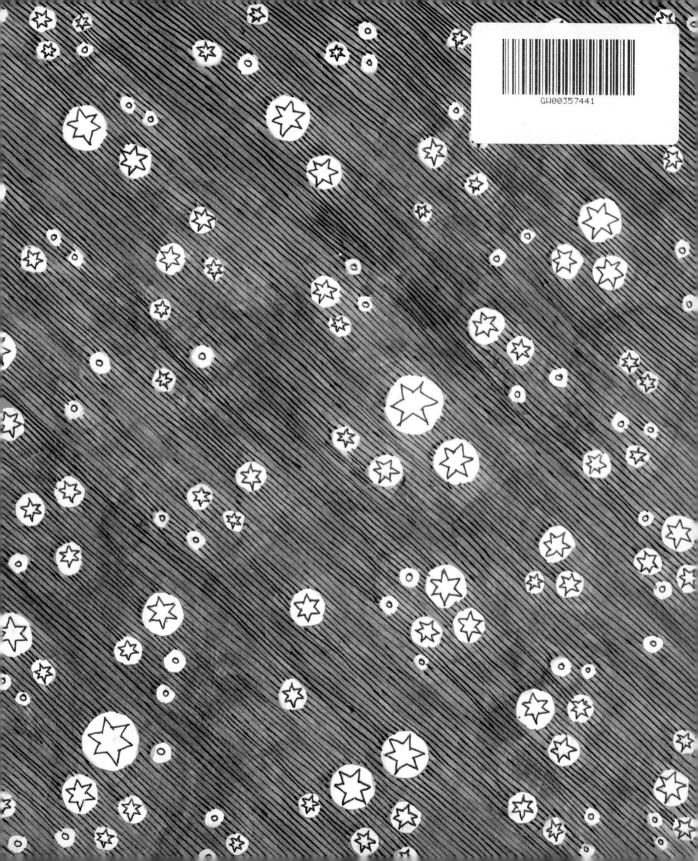

To my parents,
and for Rosy

British Library Cataloguing in Publication Data
Johnson, Jane, 1951-
   My bedtime rhyme.
   I. Title
   823'.914[J]   PZ7

   ISBN 0-86264-162-4

MY
BEDTIME RHYME

Jane Johnson

Andersen Press · London
Century Hutchinson of Australia

One night I lay in bed
And couldn't go to sleep.
I watched the moonlight moving
Making monster shadows creep.

I hid beneath the bedclothes
And the sheets shut out the light.

When I opened up my eyes again...

The whole world was all white!

I rushed around a reindeer
And then raced out of reach.

I jumped into a basket

And ballooned above a beach.

I nodded to a nestling

And it nipped me on the nose.

I dropped onto a donkey…

And disturbed it from its doze.

I fell among some hissing snakes.

A tiger snarled at me.

I thought I heard a crocodile
And stood up to try and see.

Then I met a mad old magpie,

Chased the moon

with all my might

And woke up in broad daylight!

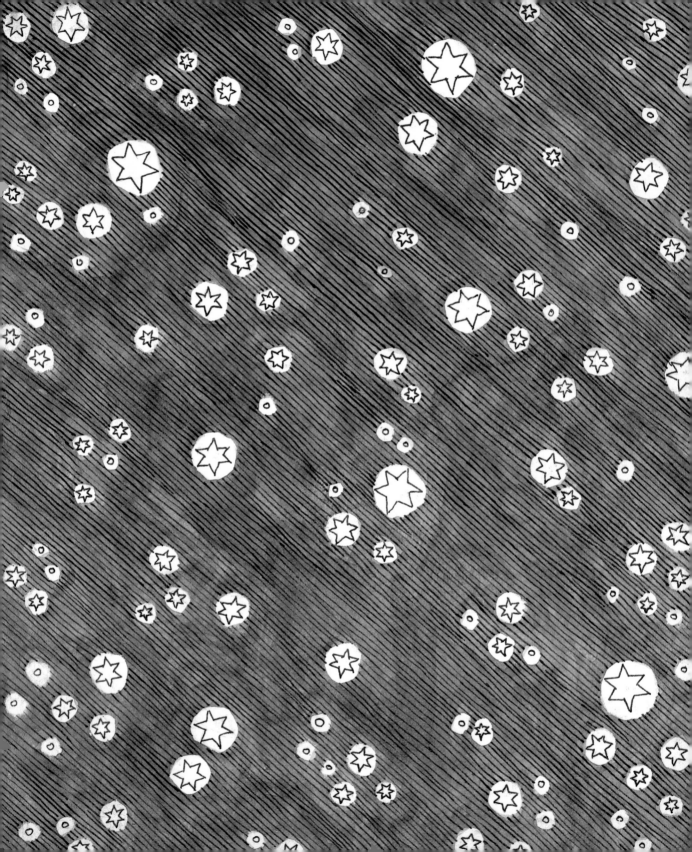